SING MUSICAL THEATRE

FOUNDATION (GRADES 1–3)

WOULDN'T IT BE LOVERLY?

AND 14 OTHER SONGS FROM THE SHOWS

Selected and edited by John Gardyne and Luise Horrocks

TRINITY
COLLEGE LONDON

FABER *ff* MUSIC

	PAGE	TRACK

All best efforts have been made to identify, contact and secure licences from copyright owners in all territories where this publication is being made available for sale. If you are a copyright owner of a work contained herein and believe that you have not been contacted for a licence, then we will be happy to rectify this promptly upon notification. Any errors or omissions will be corrected in subsequent editions.

© 2011 by Faber Music Ltd and Trinity College London
First published in 2011 by Faber Music Ltd in association with Trinity College London
Bloomsbury House
74–77 Great Russell Street
London WC1B 3DA
Music processed by SEL Engraving
Cover design by Lydia Merrills-Ashcroft
Printed in England by Caligraving Ltd
All rights reserved

CD produced and arranged by Paul Honey
© 2011 by Faber Music Ltd and Trinity College London
℗ 2011 by Faber Music Ltd and Trinity College London

ISBN10: 0-571-53556-9
EAN13: 978-0-571-53556-9

To buy Faber Music and Trinity publications or to find out about the full range of titles available,
please contact your local music retailer or Faber Music sales enquiries:

Faber Music Ltd, Burnt Mill, Elizabeth Way, Harlow, CM20 2HX England
Tel: +44(0)1279 82 89 89   Fax: +44(0)1279 82 89 90
sales@fabermusic.com   fabermusicstore.com

INTRODUCTION

In this book we have chosen 15 songs from a wide variety of shows and movies – some very well known, others less so – all of which offer specific performing challenges suitable for foundation-level singing and musical theatre students.

The best musical theatre songs are little plays with a beginning, a middle and an end. During the course of the song a character or group of characters will explore an idea, learn something, make a decision or change in some way. It is the performer's job to convey this to the audience with clarity, conviction and understanding.

In order to do this it is essential that the performer knows where the character is, what is happening in the story at that point, who the character is singing to and why s/he is expressing those ideas at that moment. So in the **BACKGROUND** to each song we have provided some key information about plot, characters and the dramatic situation, along with a brief summary of the history of the musical from which it comes.

The **PERFORMANCE NOTES** offer some starting points for interpretation and performance. Many of the observations and acting approaches can be applied to other songs in the collection (and indeed elsewhere), so we hope that as students and their teachers explore the different songs in the book they will develop a variety of approaches to preparation and rehearsal which they can start to apply to a range of repertoire.

The **SINGING TIPS** suggest some technical exercises appropriate to the particular style or demands of each song. The intention is that over time these will help students build up a range of techniques which will help develop their singing along with their acting and movement skills.

Each introduction ends with a section entitled **BEYOND THE SONG** which reflects on one key aspect of the song and suggests topics for further discussion. Some of these relate specifically to performance, others to historical, social or environmental issues which we hope will stimulate students to relate their performance work to the wider world.

The CD contains backing tracks for each of the 15 songs. While these may be used in performance, they are intended primarily as an aid to rehearsal and preparation. Again, tempi and dynamics provide a starting point only and are not intended to be 'definitive'. Performers who have the opportunity to work with a piano accompanist should explore the musical possibilities of each score, which will enable them to further refine and nuance their performances and to make them uniquely personal, uniquely their own.

Above all we hope you enjoy singing and performing these songs – and that your audience enjoy watching you do so.

John Gardyne
Chief Examiner in Drama and Speech Subjects, Trinity College London

Luise Horrocks
Singing teacher and Associate Chief Examiner, Trinity College London

VOCAL WARM-UPS
SOME SUGGESTIONS

Good singing in any style requires good physical control. Just like an athlete preparing for a run, a warm-up for the body and the voice before you start singing is essential.

- Start with a wake up and shake up! Tension in the wrong place is not good for singers so some movement to loosen up is a good place to start. Try the following:

  Wriggle the ankles, legs, wrists and arms.

  Lift and lower the shoulders then move the head gently from side to side. Swing the arms and try different swimming strokes – front crawl, back crawl and breast stroke.

  Jog on the spot.

- When you feel suitably loose, find your singing position. You should stand upright but not stretched with the head nice and central and the weight held evenly between the feet. Don't tense the knees or lift the shoulders.

- Now you are ready to have some fun vocalising! Sing the word 'sing' on a low note and hold the *ng* sound. Now, on the *ng* sound sing up and down like the siren on a police car. Gradually extend the range of the notes so that you 'siren' through your entire range. Keep the sound gentle but try not to let it crack. Then do the same on a *zz* sound like a bee buzzing. Then make sounds like an excited monkey, from the bottom of your voice to the top.

- The voice should now be getting ready to sing, so you just need to make sure that you are able to breathe from the right place, and with control. Put your fingers under your waist band or belt and cough gently. Can you feel the muscles move? These muscles need to work when you breathe. As you breathe in your tummy will get bigger and as you breathe out your tummy will get smaller. Think of a balloon getting bigger as it fills with air.

There is plenty more to discover about breathing and lots of different exercises you can use to warm up, but these vocal notes will get you started.

A PLACE CALLED NEVERLAND

PETER PAN

BACKGROUND

This song comes from Youth Music Theatre UK's one-act version of JM Barrie's children's classic *Peter Pan*, first performed in 2008.[†] Wendy, John and Michael Darling are just like any other children living with their parents in London – until Peter Pan and Tinkerbell fly in through their bedroom window and invite them to discover the magical country of Neverland.

PERFORMANCE NOTES

A great deal happens in this song: Peter asks the children to remember a magic world they have seen in their dreams, offers to take them there, teaches them how to fly, encourages them to forget their parents and everything they have known up until that point in their lives, and come with him to a land where their childhood will never end. These are big and potentially frightening ideas, so you really need to excite Wendy and the others – and the audience of course – about the wonders of Neverland. You might try speaking the lyrics as a radio commercial or as a sports commentator or news announcer. Really paint those pictures with your voice and aim to make each detail different from the others.

Unless you're performing in a theatre with specialised equipment you obviously won't be able to actually *fly* – so you'll need to experiment with movement and staging in order to make the flying lesson in the second verse convincing. There is a real moment of 'take-off' when the music changes key at bar 75. See if you can find different ways to fill that moment with magic and wonder.

SINGING TIPS

This is a lively song, with very crisp rhythms. You will need to establish a strong sense of the underlying two beats in a bar.

Practise saying the words in the correct rhythm while you bounce an imaginary ball in time. Push the ball down with your hand on the first beat and then lift the hand up as the ball bounces back on beat 2. Start slowly and then, as your confidence grows, try speaking more quickly. Keep the ball bouncing all the time. Are you able to keep the rhythms of the song crisp yet fitting neatly into the beats?

As you sing with the accompaniment, don't let the rhythm of the chords at the beginning put you off! Keep a firm sense of pulse throughout. You could try clapping, stamping or slapping your thigh on the beat as you practise. Don't slap too hard though!

BEYOND THE SONG

Since Barrie's play was first performed in 1904, there have been many adaptations, musicals, films, sequels, prequels, reworkings and parodies of *Peter Pan*. Why do you think the story has remained so popular? What is its unique appeal?

[†] Youth Music Theatre UK was founded in 2003 and is now Britain's largest organisation providing participation in musical theatre projects and productions for young people. For more information about Youth Music Theatre UK, its Musical Theatre Library and how to perform this work, go to www.youthmusictheatreuk.org.

A PLACE CALLED NEVERLAND

MUSIC BY JIMMY JEWELL
LYRICS BY NICK STIMSON

TRACK 1

When you fall a - sleep__ you dream__ a - bout__ a place called Ne-ver-land.

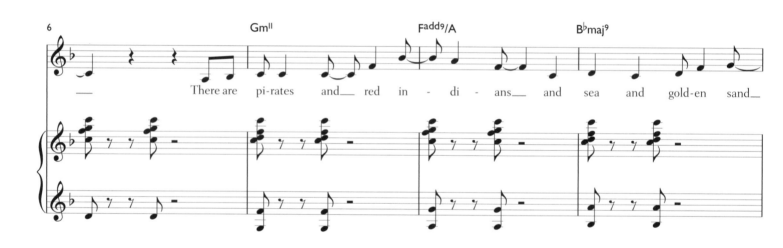

__ There are pi-rates and__ red in - di - ans__ and sea and gold-en sand__

__ and you think it's just__ a sil - ly dream__ that will fade when morn-ing breaks,__

A SPOONFUL OF SUGAR

MARY POPPINS

BACKGROUND

Walt Disney's 1964 film *Mary Poppins* is one of the most successful and best-loved movie musicals of all time. It received 13 Oscar nominations and won 5, including Julie Andrews for Best Actress in her first screen role. A stage version, rewritten with some new songs, opened in London in 2004.

London 1910: Stuffy banker Mr Banks can't control his suffragette wife or his wayward children Jane and Michael. One day the mysterious Mary Poppins flies into the children's lives. She becomes their nanny, introduces them to her friend Bert the chimney sweep, takes them on a series of magical adventures, and ends up reuniting the troubled family.

PERFORMANCE NOTES

This is a song that gives advice and teaches an important lesson. But in performance it's important that you aren't too po-faced or serious: the whole point that Mary Poppins is making is that you can have fun even when you're doing something boring and tedious, so the performance should be fun too. Enjoy it, and aim to share your enjoyment with the audience.

In this scene in the movie Mary teaches the children how to use magic to tidy up their bedroom as she sings. It is extremely difficult to create special effects of this kind on stage, so you might consider other ways of presenting the song. You might like to try performing it as different characters in different situations, maybe doing different jobs and activities. As you experiment, always be very clear about exactly who and where your characters are, what they are doing, and why they are doing it.

SINGING TIPS

This song has lots of words to fit in, and it moves at quite a quick pace. To make sure your diction is good, remember to keep all the muscles in your face nice and loose.

Run your fingers slowly and gently down your cheeks from your ears to your jaw. This will help to loosen off any tension.

Now have some fun saying made-up words. How about *lahlahloogah! piggywallah! boggerleygah!* Start by saying them slowly and then see how fast you can get without going wrong. Feel how all the muscles in your jaw are working. When you feel really confident speaking the words, try singing them. Try on one note and then on different notes. There are quite a few sections of this song using bits of scales, so run up and down small sections of scales singing your made-up words.

BEYOND THE SONG

Some of the most successful musicals of all time – *The Sound of Music*, *Oliver!*, *Annie*, *Mary Poppins* – focus on unhappy families or on lonely children looking for a family. Why do you think this is? What are the unique qualities of musical theatre that particularly suit stories of this kind?

A SPOONFUL OF SUGAR

WORDS AND MUSIC BY RICHARD M SHERMAN AND ROBERT B SHERMAN

ALONE IN THE UNIVERSE

SEUSSICAL THE MUSICAL

BACKGROUND

Seussical is a musical inspired by the popular children's books by Dr Seuss, particularly *Horton Hears a Who!* The show opened on Broadway in 2000, followed by a shorter and simpler Off-Broadway revival in 2007. A cut-down one-act 'Theatre for Young Audience' version has also proved popular.

Kind-hearted Horton the elephant discovers a tiny planet in a speck of dust, inhabited by microscopic beings called 'Whos'. Horton promises to protect the planet and puts it in a clover plant for safety. But of course all the other jungle animals just laugh at him and think he's mad. Meanwhile Jo-Jo, an inhabitant of the planet, echoes his thoughts.

PERFORMANCE NOTES

Horton, outcast and alone, is sitting by a flower which – as only he knows – contains a tiny planet. The situation is a very odd one, but you have to perform this song with absolute seriousness. Always remember that, no matter what anyone else may say, this is very important and *you are right*. Notice how Horton constantly draws a very clear distinction between himself (I've done this, I've got that) and the other animals (let them laugh, they don't know). Use this contrast to drive the song forward: let their stupidity and ignorance give you renewed self-belief. Being 'alone in the universe' isn't necessarily a bad thing – it's what makes you unique and 'gives you wings'.

The lyrics take Horton from a very small, specific spot in the jungle to wonderful imagined worlds both large and small. Experiment with staging to find ways of conveying this sense of space and potential to the audience. How much movement is necessary? How little? Does the fact that Horton is an elephant influence your physical performance?

SINGING TIPS

This song is great for trying out different dynamics. There's some repetition in the tune and the words, and it really adds to a performance if repeated phrases can be varied.

Practise some scales, up and down, singing quietly, loudly, or going from quiet to loud or loud to quiet. Do you find that you naturally tend to get quieter as you sing down a scale? Notice that many of the phrases in this song are descending phrases. Don't let the last part of the phrase disappear, especially if you're singing softly.

One extra thing to take care of here is that you don't let the words run into each other too much. For example, make sure you sing 'I'm alone' and not 'I malone', and 'They all' and not 'They yall'.

BEYOND THE SONG

When *Seussical* was first performed, critics weren't sure whether the show was aimed at children or adults. What do you think are the essential components of a children's show? Which of these might adults most enjoy?

ALONE IN THE UNIVERSE

LYRICS BY LYNN AHRENS
MUSIC BY STEPHEN FLAHERTY

TRACK
3

19

some day___ soon,___ you will hear my___ plea._____

some day___ soon,___ you will hear my___ plea._____

___ One small voice in the u - ni-verse.

One true friend in the u - ni-verse.

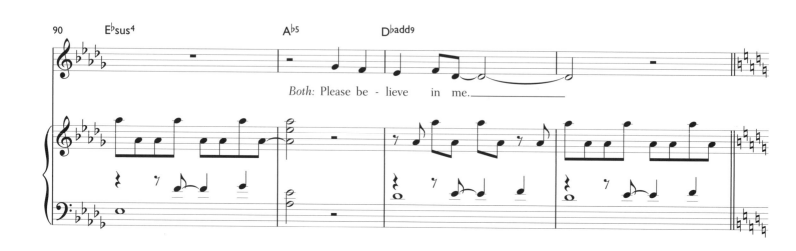

Both: Please be - lieve in me._____

COLDER NOW

THE BEES KNEES

BACKGROUND

Originally commissioned by the City of London School for Girls, *The Bees Knees* was first performed in June 2005 by a cast of 120 children between the ages of 7 and 11.[†]

The Bees Knees is set in and around a beehive. When after many years of happy rule the old Queen dies, nobody can decide who should succeed her. They eventually agree to elect one of the drones to be King. The only person to object to this is a shy young bee called Phoebe, who bravely speaks out at a public meeting. The other bees shout her down and she is banished from the hive. As night draws in, Phoebe prepares to leave her home and seek her fortune in the outside world.

PERFORMANCE NOTES

You can perform Phoebe's brief exchange with Mrs Boddle – a motherly worker bee – to put the song in context. Alternatively, sing the song as a solo piece starting at bar 11.

This is a sad song. Phoebe is heartbroken that the family that she was part of only this morning has turned against her and has thrown her out of the only home she has ever known. But she's putting a brave face on it and vows to return one day. Try acting the scene being very sad and despairing, and then being upbeat and positive. Aim to find a balance between those two emotions as you perform the song.

The music continues for four bars after the singing ends. How might you silently convey the emotions Phoebe is feeling at this moment?

SINGING TIPS

This song has a wide range of notes, from low to high. Look through and find the lowest note and the highest note. Try singing these two notes on an *oo* sound one after the other and see how different they feel. Now start with the highest and, still singing *oo*, swoop all the way down to the lowest. Really let the voice glide between the notes – aim for one long continuous sound. Once you feel comfortable with this, try doing the same from the lowest to the highest.

BEYOND THE SONG

Bees play a vital role in maintaining our natural environment by transferring pollen between flowers. But all over the world, bees are dying out because of pollution, insecticides, intensive farming techniques and the destruction of their natural habitat. The great scientist Albert Einstein is reported to have said: 'If the bee disappears off the surface of the globe, then man would only have four years of life left.' Do you think he might be right?

[†] All enquiries regarding performance rights for *The Bees Knees* should be sent to drama@trinitycollege.co.uk.

COLDER NOW

WORDS BY JOHN GARDYNE
MUSIC BY MATTHEW MILLER

TRACK
4

Mrs Boddle: You've got the chance to do something different, something special, something no bee before you has ever been able to do. The rest of us will spend the rest of our lives wondering what's out there in the big wide world. But you're going to find out. And one day you'll look back at this moment and know that this was all for the best.

Phoebe: Promise?   Mrs Boddle: I promise (hugs Phoebe). You'd best get going before nightfall. Take care of yourself won't you Phoebe?

Phoebe: Yes.   Mrs Boddle: Promise?   Phoebe: I promise. (Mrs Boddle leaves).   Phoebe: 1. It's get - ting

sky, _____ they nev - er tell you if you'll ev - er find one. _____ There's no - thing

more to say, no time for cry - ing, so thanks for hav - ing me, I must be fly - ing. Though this is so

hard to bear, as I stand here now I swear I'll some day find my way back

home.

CURIOUSER
ALICE IN WONDERLAND

BACKGROUND

Lewis Carroll's novel has charmed generations of readers since it first appeared in 1865. There have been many stage, film, opera and TV adaptations. This song comes from the 1986 musical version by Carl Davis and John Wells.

Following the White Rabbit into the rabbit hole, Alice finds herself in a strange hall with many locked doors of all sizes. Beyond one of those doors she sees an attractive garden. On a table she finds the key, but the door is too small for her to fit through. She then discovers a bottle labelled 'DRINK ME'. She does so, and she shrinks. But she can no longer reach the key on the table ...

PERFORMANCE NOTES

Before performing the song, you need to make some clear decisions so that you can engage imaginatively with this fantastical situation. Alice has just shrunk ('grown down') to a tiny size, but exactly how small do you think she is? The size of a doll? A mouse? An ant? How would the world look from down there?

When playing the role of Alice, experiment with staging and movement to give shape to the different sections of your performance. Initially you are upset and begin to cry, and your first words are quiet and tentative. But very soon the tempo and volume increase as your natural inquisitiveness takes over. Enjoy the rhythm and quickening pace of the rather old-fashioned word 'curiouser' as you take stock of your surroundings. Your thoughts change in the middle section: what will happen if you continue to shrink? Will you 'blow out like a candle' and disappear? The dramatic repeated bars 47 and 48 suggest another development – something new happening, maybe a decision being made. Consider what this might be, how you would convey it to the audience and what kind of mood you want to create in the final verse.

SINGING TIPS

Notice that the opening speed is Andante but that when the main theme returns at the end it is marked subito allegro giocoso. Find out what these Italian words mean.

This song makes particular use of semitones. Semitones can be very hard to pitch especially when singing faster. Try the following exercise, slowly at first and then, when you are more confident, more quickly:

In a comfortable part of your voice, sing up 4 semitones to the words 'I am singing up'. Then sing down the same semitones with the words 'I am singing down'. Put the two halves of the exercise together with the words 'I am singing up and singing down'. Keep listening very carefully to check that you are in tune. Make up your own words to fit – can you think of some curious things to sing about?

BEYOND THE SONG

Sir John Tenniel's original illustrations for the *Alice* books are some of the best known images from the world of children's literature, and provide most people's idea of what Wonderland looks like. What challenges do you think this familiarity presents costume and set designers – and performers – when preparing an adaptation for stage or film?

CURIOUSER

ORIGINAL TEXT BY LEWIS CARROLL
MUSIC BY CARL DAVIS
TEXT ADAPTED BY JOHN WELLS

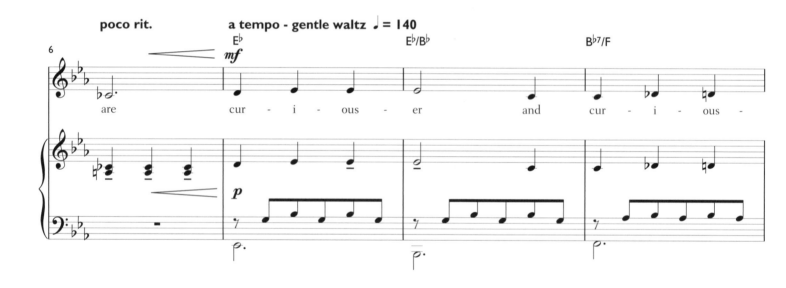

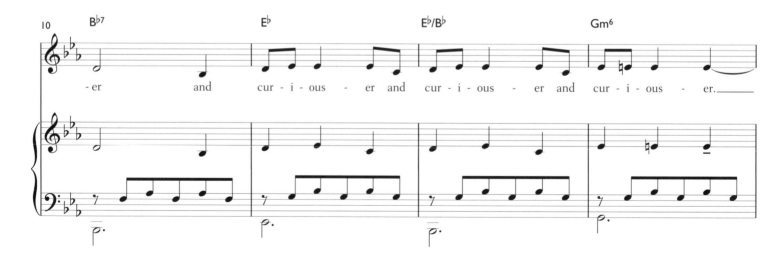

I WANT TO BE HAPPY

NO, NO, NANETTE

BACKGROUND

No, No, Nanette – a light-hearted musical comedy about the complicated home life of millionaire Bible publisher Jimmy Smith and his orphaned niece Nanette – was first performed in 1925. With its jazzy score, memorable songs, larger-than-life characters, screwball comedy and witty script, it's one of the few 1920s stage musicals that is still regularly revived today.

Jimmy's wife Sue wants Nanette to become a respectable young lady – but Nanette has a wild side and longs to experience the forbidden seaside delights of Atlantic City. When Sue makes Nanette cry by telling her that a holiday there is out of the question, Jimmy cheers her up with this infectiously tuneful song.

PERFORMANCE NOTES

When performing this song, aim to convey a sense of clarity and honesty. Note the disarmingly simple opening line, the mock-Biblical language in bars 9–11, the selfless generosity of the lyrics of the refrain ('Why can't I give some (mirth) to you?'). Always remember that the purpose of the song is to cheer up someone who is upset and unhappy.

The song can move seamlessly into dance as the performers (or performer) throw away the cares of the world and express themselves through movement – truly happy at last. And if you're going for a Twenties period style, this is a wonderful opportunity to demonstrate your tap dance skills.

For those working with an accompanist, the song can alternatively be performed as a duet for a boy and a girl using the optional additional lyrics, with Jimmy singing the first verse and Nanette replying in the second.

SINGING TIPS

This song repeats the word 'happy' many times – go through the song and count how many! *h* is an interesting consonant to sing because it can use quite a lot of air.

Try singing down a scale to *ha, ha, ha …* emphasising the *h*. What is happening to your breath? You're probably using a lot of air because air escapes before you make the *h* sound. You need to be aware of this so that you don't over-blow the *h* in 'happy' and then run out of breath. Have some fun singing the song with a very posh accent and then see if it's easier to sing with no *h* sounds – *I want to be 'appy*. Just remember that you need to put the *h* back in for the performance!

BEYOND THE SONG

The 'Roaring Twenties' (the period between the end of the First World War in 1918 and the Wall Street Crash of 1929) provided women with a new-found independence, and many flouted social norms by embracing new attitudes, lifestyles and fashion. How do you think changes in society are reflected in fashion? Or vice versa?

I WANT TO BE HAPPY

WORDS BY IRVING CAESAR
MUSIC BY VINCENT YOUMANS

TRACK 6

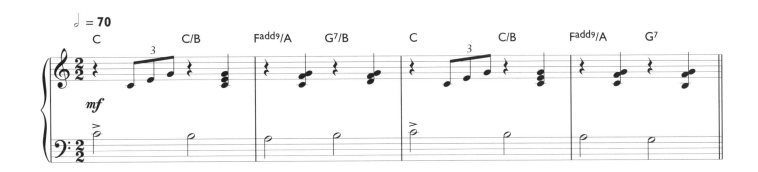

Jimmy: I'm a ve-ry or-din-ar-y man, try-ing to work out life's
Nanette: No one ev-er talked like that to me, I have nev-er known such

hap-py plan, do-ing un-to oth-ers as I'd like to have them do-ing un-to
sym-pa-thy, on-ly in my dreams, it real-ly seems to me it's too good to be

IT'S A LOVELY DAY TODAY

CALL ME MADAM

BACKGROUND

The musical comedy *Call Me Madam* premiered in New York in 1950 and starred the great Ethel Merman. She played Sally Adams, the widow of a Texas oil millionaire, who is unexpectedly appointed ambassador to the imaginary European kingdom of Lichtenburg.

While Sally develops a spikey relationship with Prime Minister Cosmo Constantin, her assistant Kenneth Gibson falls for the glamorous Princess Maria. On their first meeting they duet in this charming ballad.

PERFORMANCE NOTES

The lyrics of this song are wonderfully bright and non-committal. The invitation to share a 'lovely day' doing 'whatever you've got to do' – but if you're busy (or don't like me) that's fine too – is generous and heartfelt and floats on top of the jaunty melody as light as air.

The song provides an excellent starting point for building a character through improvisation. Try speaking the lyrics as dialogue with an acting partner. Split them up in different ways. Experiment with inventing characters of different status from different backgrounds and then putting them in a variety of situations: at a formal function, at a party, at work, on a park bench. How does the tone of the conversation alter in these different settings? Who takes the lead? Who feels in control?

The song also offers wonderful opportunities for dancing in a number of styles – solo, duet or group. The duet performed by Donald O'Connor and Vera-Ellen in the 1953 movie version of the show is considered one of the finest dance sequences ever filmed – you might want to watch it for inspiration.

SINGING TIPS

This song has long phrases, and sometimes there are high notes at the ends of lines, just when the breath is running out! To help to work the muscles that control your breathing, try the following:

Gently hum a note that is well within your range and get someone to count while you hum. See if you can hold the note to 8 comfortably. Practise this a few times and then, on one note, sing *one*, *two*, *three* etc and see if you can get to *eight*. Then sing up a scale, counting out the numbers 1 to 8 on each step. Do it fairly fast to start with and then slow it down. Make sure you don't get tense as you get higher, keeping the air flowing freely. If you feel really confident when you reach the top of the scale, hold the last note for a while!

BEYOND THE SONG

Dance sequences in 1940s and 1950s movie musicals were generally filmed in a small number of quite lengthy takes, rather than in the rapid, edited style we're used to today. What do you think this achieves? What does it tell us about the acting and dance skills of the performers at that time?

IT'S A LOVELY DAY TODAY

WORDS AND MUSIC BY IRVING BERLIN

TRACK
7

MR MISTOFFELEES

CATS

BACKGROUND

Given the legendary status of *Cats* in the history of musical theatre, it's difficult to believe that when plans for the show were first announced it was considered a wild and risky experiment. Few critics thought that the public would be interested in going to see poems from *Old Possum's Book of Practical Cats* by heavyweight poet TS Eliot set to music by Andrew Lloyd Webber. Of course they were wrong!

In this song from Act 2, Rum Tum Tugger introduces the mysterious Mr Mistoffelees to his fellow cats.

PERFORMANCE NOTES

In most productions of *Cats*, Mr Mistoffelees demonstrates his magical powers through dance as Rum Tum Tugger sings about him. Clearly the descriptions of his movements ('He can creep through the tiniest crack / He can walk on the narrowest rail') – and of course the fact that he is a *cat* – can provide rich material for choreography and animal movement work, for both groups and individuals.

The song may be sung by one or by many performers. If you're working on it as a solo, try playing a fairground 'barker' encouraging as many customers as possible to come and see this phenomenal performer. Emphasise the amazing tricks they will see: he's a conjurer, ventriloquist, acrobat and illusionist all rolled into one.

If you perform the song as a group, imagine that you're customers who have seen Mr Mistoffelees in action and who are now trying to explain to each other or to your friends the incredible things you've seen. Make each new astonishing trick top the one that precedes it – and make sure everyone listens and reacts to whoever is singing. Then join in the chorus all together with a shared sense of dazed amazement: was there ever – could there ever have been – a cat so clever?

SINGING TIPS

This song needs two different types of tone. The opening section gets big and strong. Try holding your arms out as you sing up the opening arpeggios so that you feel the sound is wide and full, not narrow and squeezed. Don't shout as you sing but keep lots of energy going.

To prepare for the next section, first whisper the words, starting with 'he is quiet, he is small, he is black'. Imagine a stage whisper where you still have to be heard at the back of a big hall. Keep your energy levels high to maintain your audience's interest.

BEYOND THE SONG

Amateur actors may only play a role for a handful of performances, but professionals will often do so for months, even years on end. One actress, Marlene Danielle, performed in the Broadway production of *Cats* for its entire run from 1982 until 2000. What do you need to do to keep your performances fresh and spontaneous every time you walk out on stage?

MR MISTOFFELEES

TEXT BY TS ELIOT
MUSIC BY ANDREW LLOYD WEBBER

TRACK 8

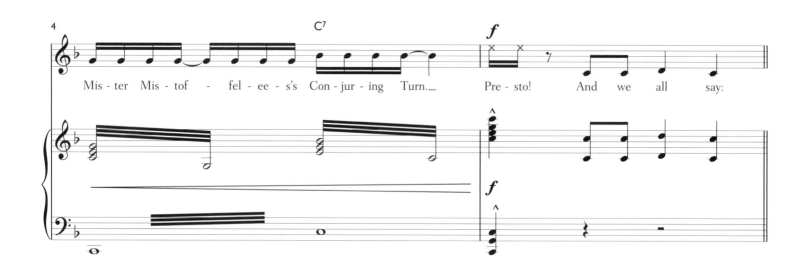

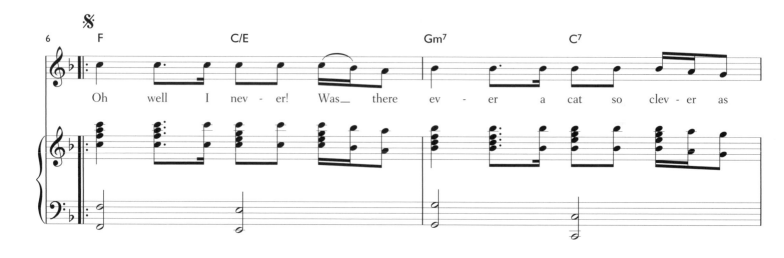

NO ONE KNOWS WHO I AM

JEKYLL & HYDE

BACKGROUND

Robert Louis Stevenson's classic story tells how respectable London surgeon Dr Jekyll's experiments into the nature of good and evil lead to his transformation into the terrible Mr Hyde. The book caused a sensation on its publication in 1886 and the first of many stage adaptations appeared a year later. Frank Wildhorn started work on his musical version in the late 1980s but it took 10 years to reach Broadway, playing over 1,500 performances from 1997–2001.

Lucy, a singer at the dingy 'Red Rat' pub in Victorian London, longs to make something of her life. As she prepares to give yet another performance, she reflects on her situation.

PERFORMANCE NOTES

This is a slow, serious number, sung by a professional singer in a rare moment of peace and quiet. Although the mood is reflective, it's important not to let your performance become a lament filled with gloom and self-pity. Lucy expresses her feelings about the emptiness of her life in lines like 'It's such a shame / I'm such a sham', but this doesn't necessarily mean she accepts that things will always be like this.

Think carefully about the section where she considers whether she is the 'face of the future', the 'face of the past' or 'the one who must finish last'. These are big, complex ideas. Do you think this is the first time Lucy has thought about such things? If so, how might you convey this to your audience? And how might this change your delivery of the final verse?

Right at the end of the song a new character is mentioned – 'you'. Who does this refer to? Experiment with different ideas until you find one you're happy with.

SINGING TIPS

This song has a rather dark feel, and this is partly due to the fact that it's in a minor key. The third note in a minor scale is very important: try practising humming up and down the first five notes of a minor scale, concentrating on the sound of the third note each time.

Sometimes singing in a minor key can mean that you lose energy. Try moving around when you're practising this song, using big arm swings and taking up lots of space if you have room. You could even try conducting in three beats with big gestures: this will ensure that you keep feeling the flow of the music.

BEYOND THE SONG

Years before it reached the Broadway stage, Frank Wildhorn released a recording of *Jekyll and Hyde* which sold 250,000 copies – so thousands of people came to the first production already knowing the music. For a theatre audience, what is the difference between hearing a song for the very first time and hearing one that is very familiar? How do you think this affects their reaction to a show?

NO ONE KNOWS WHO I AM

WORDS BY LESLIE BRICUSSE
MUSIC BY FRANK WILDHORN

TRACK
9

-vive, who will give a damn,_____ if no one knows who I

am._____ No - bo - dy knows, not ev - en you.

No one knows who I am._____

SO YOU WANNA BE A BOXER

BUGSY MALONE

BACKGROUND

Bugsy Malone is a 1976 movie musical set in Prohibition-era New York and features a cast of rival gangsters, molls, small-time hoods, chorus girls and saucy vamps. Children played all the roles, giving the film a quirky charm that is unique.

When Bugsy is set upon by a gang of hoodlums, he's saved by timid Leroy Smith who fights off his attackers. Bugsy realises that Leroy could become a champion boxer and takes him to the gym to get trainer Cagey Joe to check him out.

PERFORMANCE NOTES

This is an excellent song to stage with a group. The dramatic situation, the characters and the mood are very clear – and, most interestingly, the central character does not speak or sing at all.

In the verses the cool, professional Joe addresses Leroy directly. The tone of Joe's questions imply that his ambitions are hopelessly misguided and as the song progresses the silent, nervous Leroy feels his fragile confidence melting away. Then, to make it worse, in the chorus the other boxers plead with Joe to give them 'something new to punch'.

If you're preparing this as a solo, experiment with other ways of staging the song. Joe calling to the audience for volunteers maybe? Or what if Leroy is singing to himself in a mirror? Why might he do that? What thoughts would go through his head and why? And of course – as films like *Million Dollar Baby* have shown – girls can be boxers as well as boys.

Boxers need a combination of speed, grace and strength to succeed. Leroy will have to 'move like a hummingbird's wing', to 'bob, weave, fake and deceive'. You might use the shuffling rhythm of the song to create appropriate footwork and arm and body movements.

SINGING TIPS

This is a song with a very strong beat, and it's important to keep the words very crisp. As you sing, punch the air in time with the song, seeing how much effort this takes. Remember not to let your shoulders lift and ensure that you're breathing freely.

Your back muscles are important for good breathing. Try leaning over and placing your hands on the back of your waist. Can you feel them move as you breathe in? To help all the breathing muscles work a little harder, make a sound like a motorbike revving up to a *vvvvv* sound.

BEYOND THE SONG

People often use the language of theatre to describe sporting contests: a 'great performance', the 'twists and turns of the plot', 'the final act' and so on. What similarities and differences do you see between sport and theatre? Are there ways you could use these in your acting work?

SO YOU WANNA BE A BOXER

WORDS AND MUSIC BY PAUL WILLIAMS

Steady 4 ♩ = 108

Joe: So you wan-na be a box-er in the gold-en ring.

Can you punch like a south-bound freight train? Tell me just one thing— can you

THE GIRL I MEAN TO BE
THE SECRET GARDEN

BACKGROUND

The Secret Garden was published in 1911 and has since been adapted many times for movies, television and stage. This song comes from the 1991 version.

When her parents die in a cholera epidemic in India, 11-year-old Mary Lennox is sent to live with her uncle Archibald – a moody hunchback – in gloomy Misselthwaite Manor in Yorkshire. Mary is a lonely but imaginative child and the ghosts of her dead parents and her aunt often appear on stage to guide and comfort her. Act 2 begins with an imaginary birthday party for Mary: everyone's there, the living and the dead, 'exactly the way Mary would like to see them'. In this moment of calm and happiness, she sings 'The girl I mean to be'.

PERFORMANCE NOTES

This song really takes us inside Mary's head. Safe within her imagined world, she explores her innermost feelings about how she can face up to her new life without her parents. You might like to compare Mary's list of things that she wants with Eliza Doolittle's in 'Wouldn't it be loverly?' (see p 81). What does that tell you about the similarities and differences between the two characters?

Although this song is set within a dream, there's no need to be 'dreamy' in your delivery of the lyrics. Mary is a serious girl and her ideas are very clearly expressed. What frame of mind do you think she's in when she sings this song? What do you think she feels about her past? And her future? Does she reach a conclusion?

SINGING TIPS

Your singing in this song needs to be very smooth. The musical word for smooth is *legato*, and singing with a good legato line means that the notes must flow into each other. This means making the vowel sounds nice and long, so don't be in too much of a hurry to reach the final consonant of the word.

A good way to practise singing legato is to imagine that you're painting as you're singing. Think of your favourite colour and then think of putting your hands in a big pot of paint. As you sing the song, use your hands to make big painting strokes on an imaginary canvas in front of you. Really use all the space on your canvas and paint lovely long lines and shapes with your hands. Move your body as you do it and don't be shy! You will begin to feel how the lines in the music flow and how smooth they are.

BEYOND THE SONG

Different buildings have different acoustic properties. How might this song sound in a big house like Misselthwaite Manor, with wood-panelled walls and high ceilings? When you get the chance, try singing in different buildings – and outside too – to get a sense of how different environments can alter the way your voice sounds.

THE GIRL I MEAN TO BE

WORDS BY MARSHA NORMAN
MUSIC BY LUCY SIMON

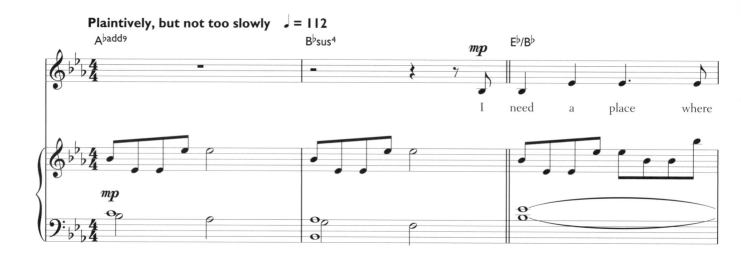

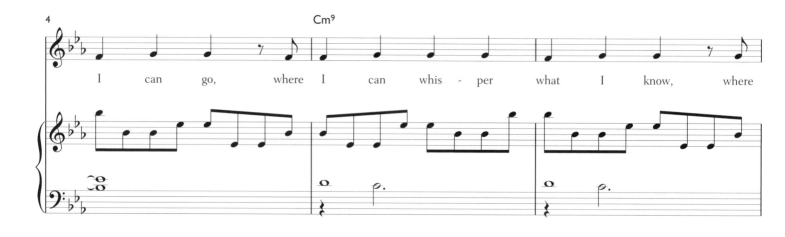

UNDER THE SEA
THE LITTLE MERMAID

BACKGROUND

Hans Christian Andersen's 1837 fairy tale *The Little Mermaid* is about a mermaid who gives up her voice and then her life for the love of a human prince. Walt Disney's 1989 animated film changed the original story's tragic ending: in this version the mermaid Ariel lives happy ever after with Prince Eric.

As Ariel dreams of visiting the human world, Sebastian the Jamaican crab tells her why life under the sea is 'better than anything they got up there'.

PERFORMANCE NOTES

'Under the Sea' is a *character song* – a song in which the lyrics, melody and mood let the performer express his or her ideas with real clarity and assurance. The jaunty calypso beat here perfectly matches Sebastian's exuberant personality and his love of music.

Notice how Sebastian constantly compares life on dry land to life underwater. Use these contrasts to energise the song. Experiment with performing the lyrics as a TV commercial for a holiday resort – really 'sell' the idea of life under the sea. Relish the witty images and rhymes ('better/wetter', 'newt/flute'). Make each new feature – the different fish, the instruments of the band, the dances – better, more surprising and more enjoyable than the one before.

SINGING TIPS

This is a really rhythmic song, and your singing needs to be very crisp to convey the feeling of jumping around. A good way to start is to say the words out loud in rhythm. Can you clap the pulse at the same time? Start by clapping a good strong beat and then say the words over your beat. Don't forget to carry on counting when you get to the rests.

When singing this song, try practising some *staccato* work. This means keeping the notes very short. Try the following exercise: Sing down a scale, making each note staccato: *The – Sea – weed – is – so – bright – and – green!* Or *The – hap – py – fish – dey – roll – a – long!* See if you can make up your own words to fit the staccato scale using ideas from the song.

BEYOND THE SONG

When the stage version of *The Little Mermaid* opened on Broadway in 2007, some critics and audience members were disappointed with the set and costume designs and felt that the magic of the undersea world was lost. Was this inevitable? What are the strengths and weaknesses of animated film and stage performance? What can one do that the other can't?

UNDER THE SEA

WORDS BY HOWARD ASHMAN
MUSIC BY ALAN MENKEN

TRACK
12

The sea-weed is al-ways green-er in some-bo-dy else-'s lake.
Down here__ all the fish is hap-py as off__ through the waves dey roll.

You dream a-bout go-ing up there. But that__ is a big mis-take.
The fish__ on the land ain't hap-py. They sad__ 'cause they in the bowl.

WE'RE OFF TO SEE THE WIZARD
THE WIZARD OF OZ

BACKGROUND

Dorothy, the Wicked Witch of the West, the Scarecrow, the Tin Man, the Cowardly Lion ... *The Wizard of Oz* features some of the most famous characters in children's literature. The 1939 movie is one of the greatest films ever made and there have been several stage adaptations since, most of which have usually included the classic songs from the movie.

A tornado transports Kansas farm girl Dorothy and her dog Toto to the magical land of Oz. The Good Witch Glinda informs her that only the Wizard can help her get back home, so she sets off along the Yellow Brick Road to the Emerald City to find him. On her way she meets three companions who join her on her journey.

PERFORMANCE NOTES

This is a bright, upbeat song full of hope and optimism. It's a song about setting out on a journey right now, so be decisive and clear from the outset ('We're *off* to see the wizard'). It's almost impossible to imagine this being performed by someone standing still: the tempo is fast and demands quite rapid movement, but creating a dance routine that gives the impression of marching happily down a road without actually leaving the stage will present an interesting challenge!

In the movie the song is repeated several times – as a duet, a trio and a quartet – each time one of Dorothy's new friends joins the group. If you're working in a group you might try out different styles of movement for the Scarecrow, the Tin Man and the Lion, exploring the similarities and differences between them.

SINGING TIPS

Lots of the energy in this song comes from the repeated ♩ ♪ rhythms. Try the following exercise to feel the 'bounce'.

Using the ♩ ♪ rhythm, sing up and down a scale: *Scoo-bee, doo-bee, doo-bee, doo-bee, doo-bee, doo-bee, doo-bee doo.* Singing one syllable on each note means that the crotchet will always be on the *oo* sound and the quaver will be on the *ee* sound. Keep the consonants crisp to give you a really strong rhythm.

Notice too how often the *w* sound is used in this song (words like 'wizard', 'wonderful', 'was'). Your lips need to be active to sing this consonant, so try saying the following: *Why wouldn't William's whistle work?* Feel what your lips are doing. Make up your own exercise using words that start with *w* and, after saying the words, make up a tune to sing them to!

BEYOND THE SONG

Over the years there have been several adaptations and sequels to *The Wizard of Oz*, including *The Wiz* and *Return to Oz*. Few people predicted the huge worldwide success of the 2003 musical *Wicked*, which turned the story upside down and re-told the story of the witches from a completely new perspective. When exploring new plays, stories and songs, never be afraid to try out big, bold, imaginative ideas – no matter how wacky they may seem. Who knows what you'll end up with?

WE'RE OFF TO SEE THE WIZARD

MUSIC BY HAROLD ARLEN
LYRICS BY EY HARBURG

TRACK 13

wiz' there was, the Wiz-ard of Oz is one be-cause, be - cause, be-cause, be - cause, be-cause, be -

- cause, be - cause of the won-der - ful things he does.

We're off to see the Wiz-ard, the won-der-ful Wiz-ard of Oz.

We're

WHO WILL BUY?

OLIVER!

BACKGROUND

Lionel Bart's musical adaptation of Charles Dickens' 1838 novel *Oliver Twist* was an immediate hit when it was first performed in London 1963. It transferred to Broadway for a record-breaking run and was made into an Oscar-winning movie.

The story is set in London in the early 19th century. Young orphan Oliver Twist is thrown out of the workhouse for daring to ask for a second helping of gruel. He falls in with a gang of thieves led by the villainous Fagin, who teaches him how to be a pickpocket. But on his first attempt, Oliver is captured trying to steal from a rich elderly man called Mr Brownlow, who takes pity on him and takes him into his own home. The next day, as he awakes to the cries of street sellers offering milk, roses and strawberries for sale, Oliver feels truly safe and happy for the first time.

PERFORMANCE NOTES

In the stage show this scene is set in the street outside Mr Brownlow's house. The song begins with solo lines sung by the street sellers at dawn. Oliver – watching from his bedroom window – joins in as the city awakes. In the movie this scene becomes an elaborate 8-minute sequence with hundreds of extras creating a rich panorama of city life.

In solo performance you might want to sing this song 'in character' as Oliver or as one of the street sellers. Whichever you choose, you will need to convey the mood and atmosphere of someone awakening to a bright and beautiful morning on which everything feels possible. How might you move around the stage – and what physical actions might you make – to convey this wonderful feeling of excitement and potential?

SINGING TIPS

Lovely long lines characterise this song. To achieve a warm, open sound, all the vowels need to be sung very smoothly. The difficulty is that, on some longer notes, you have to sing diphthongs.

A diphthong is where two vowel sounds are connected in a sort of gliding motion. For example, 'buy' is a combination of an *ar* sound and an *ee* sound. Say the word very slowly and feel the glide between the two sounds. Now sing the word on one note, really exaggerating the two different sounds. Can you hear how odd this sounds? When you sing you need to emphasise the first sound slightly and then very gently and quickly glide into the second sound so that the word is not distorted.

Can you find other words in this song that have diphthongs in them?

BEYOND THE SONG

Street cries – words and phrases shouted or sung to simple tunes by pedlars and street sellers letting people know that they have certain goods or services for sale – were one of the earliest forms of advertising. What jingles, tunes and snatches of songs do you hear on the streets nowadays? How might they combine to make a 'soundtrack' of modern city life?

WHO WILL BUY?

WORDS AND MUSIC BY LIONEL BART

TRACK
14

Who will buy this won-der-ful morn - ing?
Who will buy this won-der-ful feel - ing?

Such a sky you nev-er did see._____
I'm so high I swear I could fly!_____

WOULDN'T IT BE LOVERLY?
MY FAIR LADY

BACKGROUND

My Fair Lady is based on the 1914 play *Pygmalion* by English playwright George Bernard Shaw. When Professor Henry Higgins, a pompous language expert, encounters Eliza Doolittle selling flowers outside Covent Garden opera house, he's appalled by her cockney accent and boasts to his friend Colonel Pickering that by teaching her to speak properly he could 'pass her off as a duchess' in six months. Eliza boldly challenges him to prove it ...

PERFORMANCE NOTES

Eliza sings 'Wouldn't it be loverly?' immediately after her first meeting with Higgins and Pickering. Although her life is hard and she is very poor, she's had a good day.

Some of Eliza's daydreams are very modest. She'd like a roof over her head, a chair, and some time to rest. But of course she'd like lots of chocolate too. You might like to act out some of her daydreams while you practise. Even though her life is hard, there's no hint of self pity in the song – it's upbeat, imaginative and optimistic, just like Eliza herself. In the last verse she dreams about finding someone who will take care of her in the future. How is this different from what has gone before?

Notice how the lyrics include cockney pronunciation and phrases ('luverly', 'absobloominlutely'). The word 'loverly' is repeated several times at the end of the song. Why do you think Eliza uses this word so much? How might you vary the way you sing the word each time?

SINGING TIPS

Have some fun with the words in this song. Say them out loud and play with different accents. Try 'posh', American or Italian. Feel how the shapes of the vowels change as you speak differently. Now try singing the song with Eliza's cockney accent. Do you notice how the final consonants of words almost disappear? So that your diction stays nice and clear, make sure the beginnings of words are well projected. Don't be frightened of using your lips and tongue. Try the following exercises to loosen up these muscles:

1. With your mouth closed, run the tip of your tongue all the way round the outside of your teeth.

2. Gently chew an imaginary toffee. Make the right sounds to show that you are enjoying it.

3. Blow a few raspberries!

BEYOND THE SONG

Even though the musical is set nearly 100 years ago, today many millions of children and young people still have to struggle to survive on the streets in cities all over the world. Imagine what it would be like to be cold, dirty, hungry and alone. What would be most important to you? How would you see your future?

WOULDN'T IT BE LOVERLY?

WORDS BY ALAN JAY LERNER
MUSIC BY FREDERICK LOEWE

TRACK
15

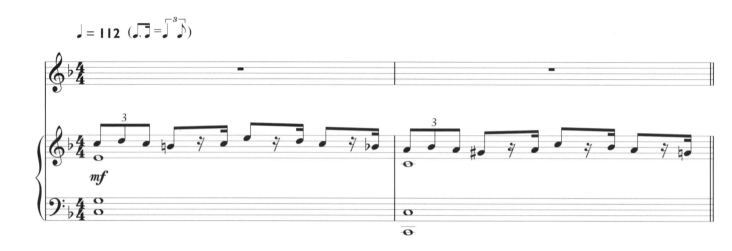

Eliza: All I want is a room some-where, far a-way from the cold night air,

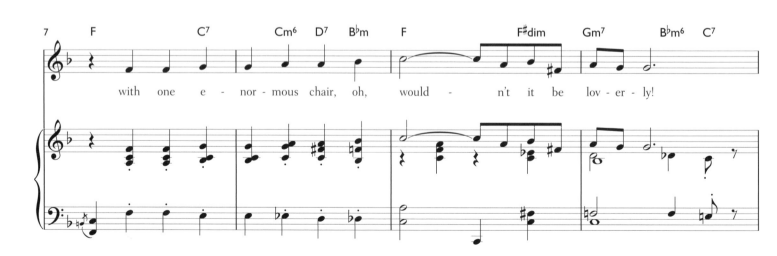

with one e-nor-mous chair, oh, would-n't it be lov-er-ly!

83

86

OTHER TITLES AVAILABLE IN THIS SERIES

 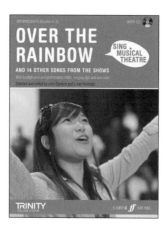 

ANY DREAM WILL DO
ISBN10: 0-571-53555-0

ANY DREAM WILL DO

BE KIND TO YOUR PARENTS

A COMMON BOY

FAT SAM'S GRAND SLAM

FLASH, BANG, WALLOP!

JUST ONE PERSON

LET'S GO FLY A KITE

A LOVELY LEGGY POTION

MAYBE

MOONSHINE LULLABY

MY FAVOURITE THINGS

PART OF YOUR WORLD

ROUND-SHOULDERED MAN

THE WASPISH TANGO

WHERE IS LOVE?

OVER THE RAINBOW
ISBN10: 0-571-53557-7

BEAUTIFUL

FEED THE BIRDS

I CAN HEAR THE BELLS

I LOVE PARIS

I WANT TO GO HOME

LEGALLY BLONDE

LES POISSONS

MY DEFENCES ARE DOWN

MY SHIP

NOTICE ME, HORTON

ONLY LOVE

OVER THE RAINBOW

REVIEWING THE SITUATION

SOMETHING GOOD

WARTS AND ALL

WHISTLE DOWN THE WIND
ISBN10: 0-571-53558-5

BRUSH UP YOUR SHAKESPEARE

BUT NOT FOR ME

CLOSE EVERY DOOR

DIFFERENT

FAR FROM THE HOME I LOVE

I COULD HAVE DANCED ALL NIGHT

I WANT TO KNOW

I'M NOT THAT GIRL

MISTER SNOW

OH, THE RIO GRANDE

OOM PAH PAH

THERE MUST BE MORE

WHEN I GET MY NAME IN LIGHTS

WHEN I LOOK AT YOU

WHISTLE DOWN THE WIND

To buy Faber Music or Trinity publications or to find out about the full range of titles available
please contact your local music retailer or Faber Music sales enquiries:

Faber Music Ltd, Burnt Mill, Elizabeth Way, Harlow CM20 2HX
Tel: +44 (0) 1279 82 89 89   Fax: +44 (0) 1279 82 89 90
sales@fabermusic.com   fabermusic.com   fabermusicstore.com